Kate and the sheep

'I wish we could have a pet,' said Kate to her mum.

'We've got Solomon,' said Mum.

'He's only a cat,' said Kate. 'We can't take him
   for walks and he won't fetch sticks.'

'We can't have a dog,' said Mum. 'Dogs chase sheep.'

1

Kate and Jo were at the village shop.
Mr Mudge was there with his dog, Gyp.
'Mr Mudge,' asked Kate, 'does Gyp chase sheep?'
'No,' said Mr Mudge, 'he's too old.
    It takes him all his time to get out of bed!'

At that moment Gyp began to bark.

Mr Munday, the farmer, was driving a flock of
  sheep through the village square.

Mr Munday walked in front with an old ewe and
  Glenn, his dog, followed them.

'Hello, Mr Munday,' said Kate. 'Where are you going?'
'I'm taking these sheep for their dinner.
  They've eaten all the grass in the little field
  and now they have to be put in the big field.'
'Can we help?' asked Jo.

'Yes, you can open the gate for me if you
    like,' said Mr Munday.
The sheep followed them up the hill.
'They are very well-behaved,' said Jo.
Glenn followed quietly behind the flock.

When they got to the big field Kate and Jo opened
  the gate and the sheep went in.
Mr Munday shut the gate and fastened it.
'That wasn't too difficult, was it?' he said.
'I hope we'll be able to help again,' said Jo.

Mr Munday laughed.

'I need all the help I can get at the moment,'
he said. 'Mrs Munday has a broken arm and
I'm having to do all the farm work myself.
I don't know what I'll do once lambing starts.'

Glenn wagged his tail and barked.

'I'd better give that dog his feed, too,' said
  Mr Munday. 'And I should think it's time you
  girls went home for yours.'

They all walked back towards the square.

'Does Glenn chase the sheep?' asked Kate.
'No, he doesn't,' laughed the farmer. 'He helps
    me look after them.'
'I wish we had a pet like Glenn,' said Jo.
'He's no pet,' said Mr Munday. 'He's a working dog.'

At dinner time Kate told Dad how they
  had helped the farmer.
'I'm glad you did,' said Dad, 'It's going to be
  a very busy time for him when the ewes
  start having their lambs.'

The girls helped Dad with the washing up.
'We're doing a lot of helping today,' frowned Jo.
'I like helping,' said Kate. 'Let's go and see
   if the sheep have finished their dinner.'
They went to the big field and climbed on the gate.

The sheep were still nibbling the grass.
They were taking a long time over their dinner.
'They must have eaten enough by now,' said Kate.
  'I expect Mr Munday will come and get them soon.'
They waited and waited but Mr Munday didn't come.

Then Kate had an idea.

'Perhaps Mr Munday is busy,' she said.

   'We could take the sheep home for him.'

Jo wasn't sure the idea was a good one.

'Do you think they will come with us?' she asked.

Kate opened the gate and they went into the field.
'Come on, sheep,' she called, 'it's time to go home.'
But the sheep went on eating.
When the girls walked towards them, the
    sheep walked away.

'We need a sheepdog,' said Jo. 'I wish we had
    Glenn here to help us.'
'You will just have to pretend to be a dog,'
    said Kate. 'Go over to the wall and bark.'
Jo crossed the field and began to make dog noises.

But the sheep just went on eating.
The old ewe was in the middle of the field.
Kate remembered how all the other sheep
   had followed it up the road.
She began to walk towards the old ewe.

The old ewe stopped eating and looked
    at Kate and Jo.
It started to walk towards the open gate, and
    then it began to run.
The other sheep ran after it.

'Can I stop barking now?' shouted Jo.
The whole flock ran out of the big
   field and down into the village.
Kate and Jo could not keep up with them.
'Stop barking, stop barking!' yelled Kate.

Mr Mudge was in the village square.
He saw the sheep running towards him with
    Kate and Jo running after them.
'Stop!' he shouted. 'Stop those sheep!'
He waved his stick at them.

The old ewe slowed down when she
  saw Mr Mudge.
But instead of stopping she turned and
  ran into the village shop.
Some of the other sheep followed her.

Soon there were sheep everywhere.
There were sheep in the churchyard and
   sheep in the village inn.
There were sheep in people's gardens and
   sheep in people's houses.

Kate and Jo were very worried.

A Land Rover came up the hill and into
the village square.

Their mum was driving it and she was very
angry when she saw what had happened.

People began to come out of their houses.
Some were cross and some were laughing.
Then Mr Munday ran up with Glenn.
It took ages to get the sheep back into the field.
Everybody had to help.

Mum made Kate and Jo say they were sorry
to Mr Munday for the trouble they had caused.
'Never mind,' he said. 'You were only trying
to help me but you must never open gates
when there are animals in the field.'

Kate and Jo started to cry.

When the farmer saw how upset the girls were
he had a quiet word with Mum.

'Get into the Land Rover,' she said. 'We're all
going down to the farmhouse.'

They drove down to the farmhouse and
  Mr Munday led the way into the kitchen.
In a basket near the fire the girls
  saw a tiny new-born lamb.
Mr Munday picked it up and got a bottle.

The lamb began to drink the milk.
'This lamb's mother won't suckle it,' said
  Mr Munday. 'It has to be fed by hand.
  I'm far too busy to look after baby lambs
  so I'd like you to look after it.'

Kate and Jo could hardly believe their luck.
'Now we can really help,' said Kate.
They wrapped the lamb in a blanket and
    took it home in the Land Rover.
Mum put it in a cardboard box near the stove.

'This lamb is not a toy,' she said. 'You are
   going to have to feed it and look after it.
   It's a big responsibility.'
'What's a responsibility?' asked Jo.
'It means we have to do it properly,' said Kate.

Kate and Jo looked after the lamb all
  through the holidays.
Every morning, before she had her own breakfast,
  Kate gave the lamb its warm milk.
The lamb seemed to take up most of the girls' time.

'I'm glad we don't have to look after
  the whole flock,' said Jo.
The lamb was soon old enough to play with
  the girls in the garden.
But it never learned to fetch a stick!

Then one day Mr Munday said that the lamb was
   old enough to go into the field with the others.
The girls were sad to see their lamb go but
   they were glad they had been able to help.
They often went to the field to watch the lambs.
But they were always careful to shut the gate.

Printed in Hong Kong